Pirate
ABC Dot-to-Dot
Adventure

Published by Top That! Publishing plc
Tide Mill Way, Woodbridge, Suffolk, IP12 1AP, UK
www.topthatpublishing.com
Copyright © 2013 Top That! Publishing plc
All rights reserved.
0 2 4 6 8 9 7 5 3 1
Printed and bound in China

It is time for summer vacation and Max and Molly are at the seaside.

While they are building sandcastles, they spot an old-fashioned sailing vessel far out at sea.

Max and Molly try to imagine what it would have been like to sail on a pirate galleon.

After lunch Max and Molly feel tired and they decide to take a nap in the shade. Suddenly, Max and Molly find themselves on the deck of a large sailing ship!

"How did we get here?" asks Max.
"And why are the crew firing the cannons?" exclaims Molly.

Join the dots to reveal what the crew
are trying to hit with their cannons.

Max and Molly are on the deck of a pirate ship!

"I think that we should hide before they notice us," says Molly. "I don't like the look of that pirate coming toward us!"

Join the dots to reveal
what Max and Molly
are hiding behind.

The fearsome pirate captain tells his crew that they have stowaways on-board! Max and Molly feel very scared as they hide behind the ship's wheel.

Join the dots
to reveal what
the pirate crew
are holding!

Max and Molly can hear the pirate captain getting closer, and closer, and closer! "Quick!" shouts Max. "Let's climb the rigging."

Max and Molly run across the deck and start to climb the rigging just before the pirate captain reaches them.

Max and Molly reach the ship's crow's nest and wonder what to do next. They are trapped!

In the distance, the ship that was being fired at has turned around and is sailing back toward the pirate ship.

h
g
f
i
e
d
c
b
a
j
k
l
m
n
o
p
q
r
s
t
u
v
w
x
y
z

What else can Max and Molly see from high up in the crow's nest?

As Max and Molly try to think what to do next, a cannonball whizzes past and smashes into the main sail. The pirate ship is under attack!

As the pirates turn their attention to the approaching enemy ship, Max and Molly sneak back down the rigging and creep below deck.

It is very dark below deck. What can Max and Molly see as their eyes get used to the dim light?

As they look around the ship's quarters, Max and Molly can hear footsteps approaching and flee above deck again. When they arrive on deck, they can see the enemy ship alongside the pirate ship. A battle is about to start!

The enemy ship belongs to the navy!
Join the dots to complete the ships.

Max and Molly crouch down by the gunpowder barrels and wait for the battle to commence.

The navy officers are armed with guns and swords. The pirates have cutlasses and daggers.

Suddenly, a cannonball blasts into the side of the pirate ship and the navy crew use ropes to board the pirate vessel.

Max and Molly watch the battle from their hiding place. Although the pirates are very tough, they are outnumbered and their cutlasses are no match for the guns of the navy. It is not long before the pirate captain is forced to surrender.

The surrendered pirates are locked up below deck and will be taken to the mainland to stand trial. As Max and Molly come out from their hiding place, the navy captain thinks they are pirates too!

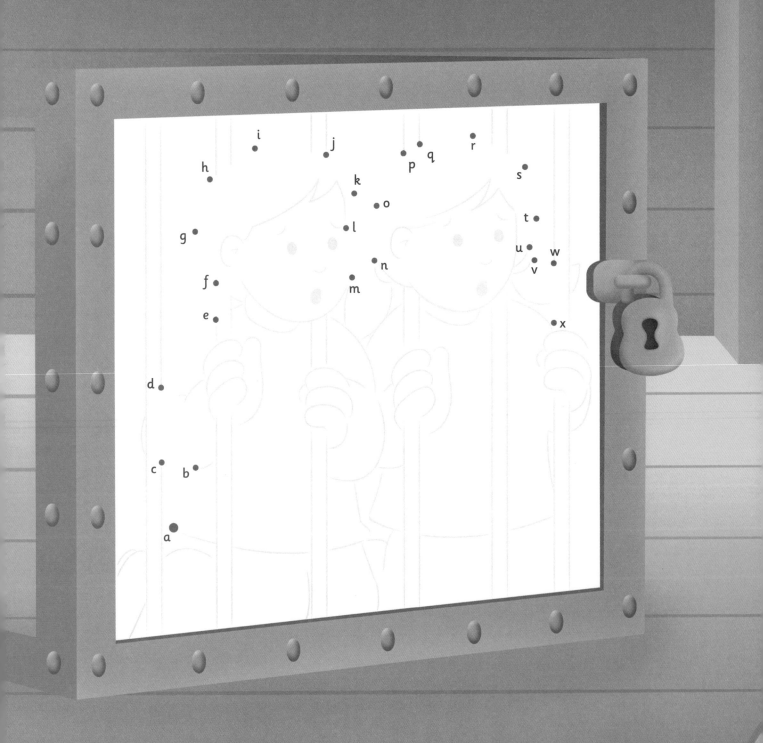

"We're not pirates!" protest Max and Molly together.

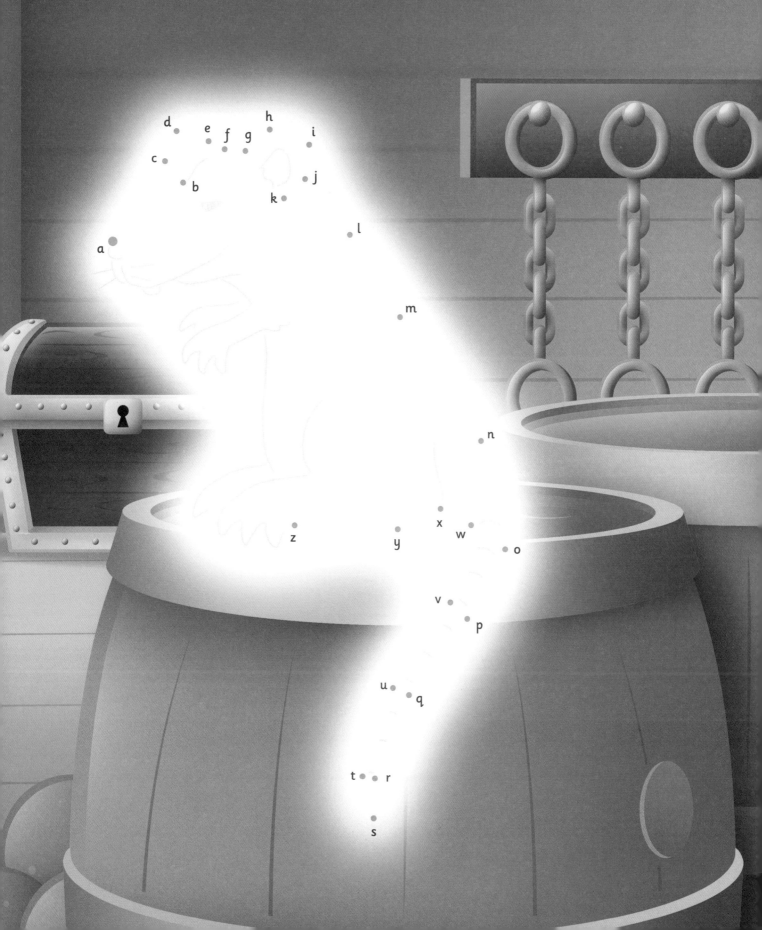

Max and Molly wake up with a jolt in the shade of a tree. They weren't really on-board a pirate ship—it was all a dream. "Phew!" say Max and Molly happily.